Sandy Creek
NEW YORK

An Imprint of Sterling Publishing
387 Park Avenue South
New York, NY 10016

Consultant: Fiona Moss RE Adviser, RE Today Services
Editor: Cathy Jones
Designer: Chris Fraser

ISBN 978-1-4351-5234-2

Manufactured in Guangdong, China
Lot #:
10 9 8 7 6 5 4 3 2 1
08/13

Noah's Ark

Written by Katherine Sully

Illustrated by Simona Sanfilippo

Sandy Creek

NEW YORK

Old man Noah was a very good man.

He loved God and always listened to what God told
him. God loved Noah because he was good.

But God was not happy with the rest of the people.
They didn't listen and behaved very badly.

One day, God said to Noah, "I am going to flood the earth to wash it clean. Build a wooden ark and make sure it will not leak.

"Take your family and two of
every kind of animal into the ark.

Bring plenty of food
for everyone. In seven days
I will make it rain."

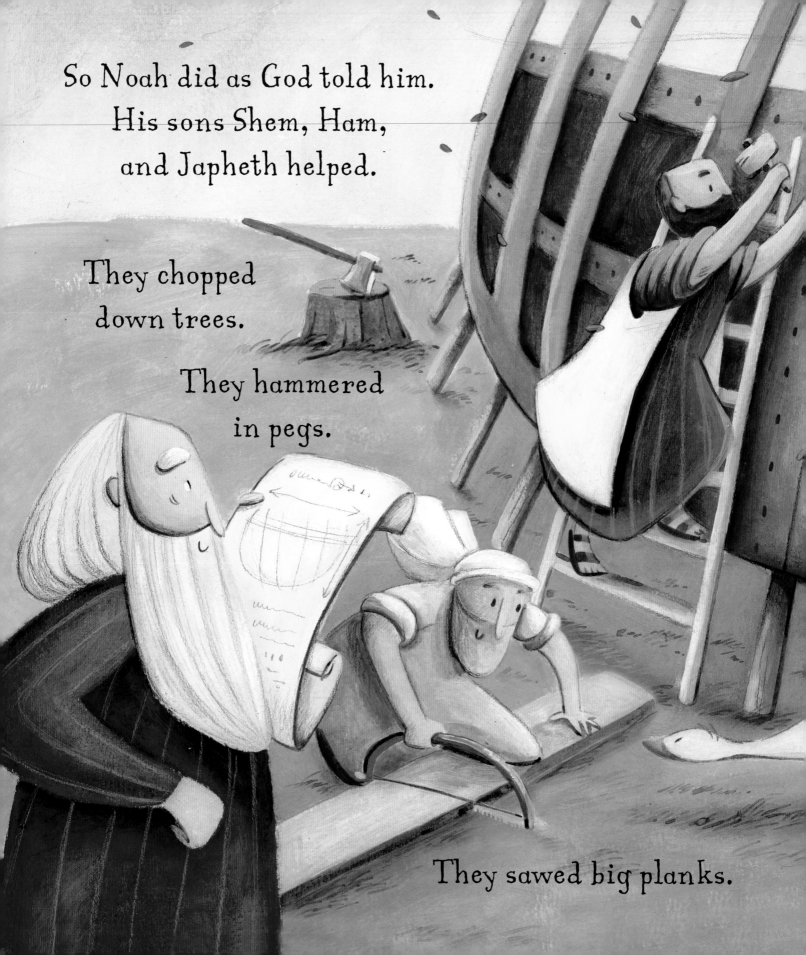

So Noah did as God told him.
His sons Shem, Ham,
and Japheth helped.

They chopped
down trees.

They hammered
in pegs.

They sawed big planks.

They painted
the ark so that it
would not leak.

They all worked very hard until the ark was finished.

But there was no time to rest.
Next, they collected two of every kind
of animal. It wasn't easy!

Two by two the
animals crept or slithered
or plodded or hopped onto the ark.

Sure enough, after seven days, it began to rain.
Drip, drop—the rain didn't stop!
The water rose and lifted the ark.

For forty days and forty nights it rained. Even the highest mountains were flooded.

Inside the ark it was dark.
All the animals squashed
together and
they made
a terrible
noise!

Squawk!

Moo!

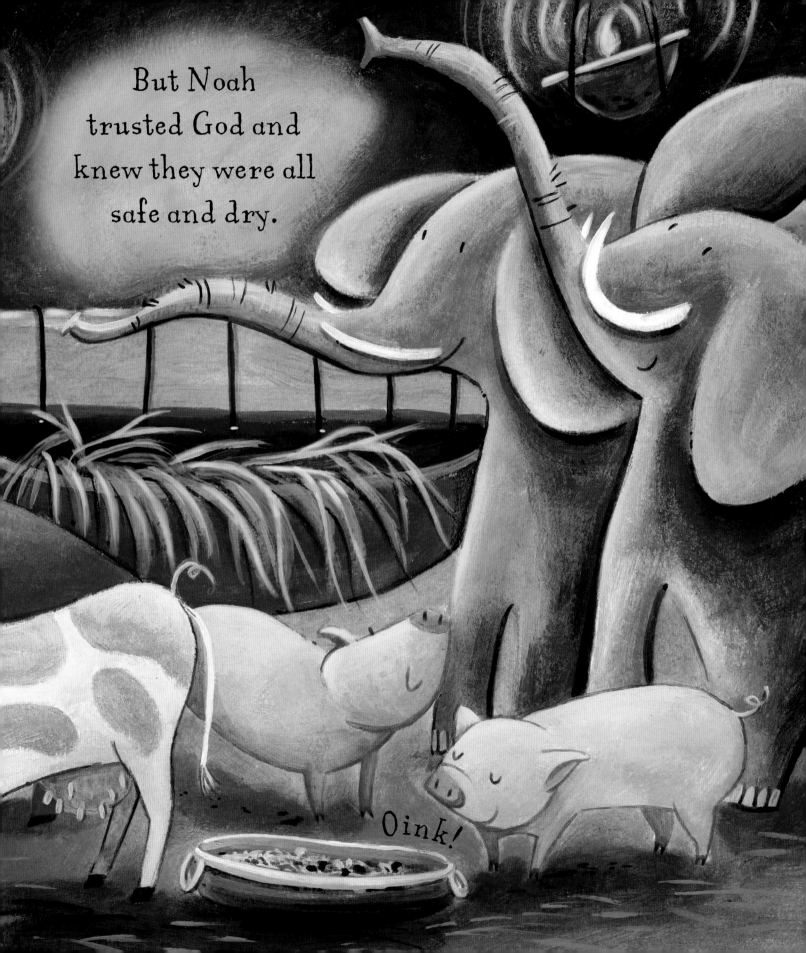

For another hundred and fifty days the earth was flooded and washed clean. But God did not forget Noah and his ark.

Drip, drop—
the rain DID stop!

Then God sent a wind
and the flood went down.
Finally, the ark landed on the
top of the highest mountain.

Slowly, the water went down and down.
Noah opened the window and saw
other mountain tops.

He sent out
a dove, but
the dove soon
flew back.

A week later,
Noah sent out
the dove again.

This time it flew back
carrying a twig in its beak.

Noah waited another week
and sent out the dove again.

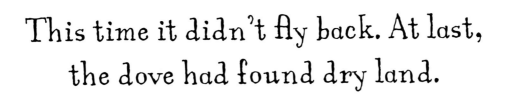

This time it didn't fly back. At last,
the dove had found dry land.

Then God said to Noah,
"It's safe to come out now."

Two by two, the animals
came out of the ark into
the sunshine.

After that, God made a promise to Noah never to flood the earth again.

As a sign of his promise,
God put a colorful rainbow in the sky.

Next Steps

Now that you've read the story...what do you remember?

* Who told Noah to build the ark?
* Why did God send the flood?
* What went into the ark?
* How long did it rain?
* Where did the ark come to rest?
* Why did God send the rainbow?

What does the story tell us?
If we listen to God, He will look after us.